CW00410906

Piano
Grade 6

Pieces & Exercises
for Trinity College London
examinations

2012-2014

Published by
Trinity College London

Registered Office:
89 Albert Embankment
London SE1 7TP UK

T +44 (0)20 7820 6100
F +44 (0)20 7820 6161
E music@trinitycollege.co.uk
www.trinitycollege.co.uk

Registered in the UK
Company no. 02683033
Charity no. 1014792

Printed in England by the Halstan Printing Group, Amersham, Bucks.

Allegro di molto

1st movement from Sonata in F minor, Wq. 63/6

Carl Philipp Emanuel Bach
(1714-1788)

Dynamics are editorial.

Allegro

1st movement from Sonatina op. 20 no. 6

Jan Ladislav Dussek
(1760-1812)

8

Menuetto and Trio

3rd movement from Sonata in D, op. 10 no. 3

Ludwig van Beethoven
(1770-1827)

(1) Editorial suggestion that the left hand plays the F♯ and E in bar 25.

Menuetto D.C.
ma senza replica

You may photocopy this page to avoid a page turn.

[Blank page to facilitate page turns]

Romance
op. 2

Joachim Raff
(1822–1882)

Canzonetta

op. 41 no. 3

Ernö Dohnányi
(1877–1960)

Stamping Dance

from *Mikrokosmos* vol. 5 SZ107

Béla Bartók
(1881–1945)

Tempi shown are composer's own.

Prelude no. 8

from *24 Preludes and Fugues* op. 87

Dmitri Shostakovich
(1906–1975)

Composer's metronome mark ♩ = **108**.

This Prelude was originally followed *attacca* by a Fugue.

Prelude no. 2

from *Five Preludes*

Christopher Headington
(1930–1996)

Composer's metronome mark ♩ = **60**. Fingerings have been suggested for examination purposes only.

Dreamy

Brian Bonsor
(born 1926)

The small notes in bars 16 and 34 are optional.
Composer's metronome mark ♩ = c. **76.**

Taken from *Jazzy Piano 2* UE19363.

26

Exercises

1a. A Sad Waltz – tone, balance and voicing

1b. Three with Four – tone, balance and voicing

2a. A Neat Idea – co-ordination

2b. A Suite Idea – co-ordination

3a. Off the Scale! – finger & wrist strength and flexibility

3b. Three-part Invention – finger & wrist strength and flexibility